W9-BYV-238

March of America Facsimile Series

Number 97

How We Built
the Union Pacific Railway

Grenville M. Dodge

How We Built the Union Pacific Railway

by Grenville M. Dodge

ANN ARBOR

UNIVERSITY MICROFILMS, INC.

A Subsidiary of Xerox Corporation

Foreword

Major General Grenville M. Dodge was one of the greatest railroad builders of the nineteenth century. He served as chief engineer of the Union Pacific during the construction of that road and his *How We Built the Union Pacific Railway*, published by the Government Printing Office in Washington in 1910, presents a short factual account of that feat. Dodge's little book provides the stark outlines of what took place, with names of participants, dates, and engineering information. As an engineer and builder, Dodge was a genius; as a writer, he was pedestrian. No glimmer of imagination enlightens his text, but he does give the facts as the chief architect of the railway saw them. For that reason the tract is important.

Dodge received his education in schools and academies in New Hampshire and Vermont. In 1852 he got a job with a surveying party on the Illinois Central Railroad and was noticed by the engineer in charge, Peter A. Dey, who took Dodge with him when he undertook surveys for the Mississippi and Missouri Railroad (later the Rock Island). Dodge was placed in charge of the survey from Davenport to Council Bluffs, completed in 1853. At Council Bluffs, Dodge made his home, and for the next few years he engaged in mercantile ventures and helped to promote railway construction. At the outbreak of the Civil War, he volunteered his services and rose to the rank of major general. He was wounded twice, at Pea Ridge and at Atlanta. Sherman and Grant both commended him highly for his gallantry in action and his skill as an engineer, specially in the construction of railway bridges.

In 1866, Dodge gave up his commission in the United States Army to become chief engineer of the Union Pacific. Grading for the road had started in December, 1863, at Omaha, but scarcity of labor and money had delayed work until the end of the war. After Dodge took over the operation, construction accelerated. Before the end of 1866, track was being laid at the rate of a mile a day, and that rate was soon surpassed. During the year 1868, Dodge drove his crews to lay 754 miles of track as far as Humboldt Wells in Utah.

The Union Pacific and the Central Pacific, which had started at Sacramento, California, were each struggling to gain distance over the other. Dodge surveyed his right-of-way to the California line, and the Central Pacific's engineers pushed on into Utah. At times the two rival railways were working parallel with each other, and the Irish labor gangs of the Union Pacific and the Chinese coolies of the Central Pacific occasionally engaged in bloody war. At last an agreement was worked out in Washington to have the two lines join at Promontory, Utah, where the famous episode of "driving the last spike" occurred on May 10, 1869. So much whiskey and champagne were consumed that the ceremony was completed with difficulty. Dodge writes with deadpan seriousness of the event: "Prayer was offered; a number of spikes were driven in the two adjoining rails, each one of the prominent persons present taking a hand, but few hitting the spikes, to the great amusement of the crowd. When the last spike was placed, light taps were given upon it by several officials, and it was finally driven home by the chief engineer of the Union Pacific Railway [Dodge himself]."

Dodge makes only oblique and defensive allusions to the scandals that beset the building of the railroads. To read his account, one would not know that promoters of the Union Pacific Railway had organized a construction company known as the Crédit Mobilier to sell to the railway at extortionate rates supplies and equipment or that they had attempted to suborn Congress. Indeed, Dodge, who himself was one of the most skillful lobbyists of his time, defended the promoters and declared them innocent of all guilt. He makes a ringing defense of one of the chief promoters, Congressman Oakes Ames, who had sold Crédit Mobilier stock to his fellow Congressmen, "where it would do us the most good," at prices much below the market value.

A succinct account of Dodge will be found in the *Dictionary of American Biography*. See also Stewart H. Holbrook, *The Story of American Railroads* (New York, 1947).

How We Built
the Union Pacific Railway

61ST CONGRESS }
2d Session }

SENATE

{ DOCUMENT
{ No. 447

HOW WE BUILT THE UNION PACIFIC RAILWAY

And Other Railway Papers and Addresses

BY

Major-General GRENVILLE M. DODGE

Chief Engineer Union Pacific Railway
1866–1870

PRESENTED BY MR. HALE

MARCH 22, 1910.—Ordered to be printed, with illustrations

WASHINGTON
GOVERNMENT PRINTING OFFICE
1910

MAJOR-GENERAL G. M. DODGE.

Chief Engineer Union Pacific Railway, 1866–1870.

HOW WE BUILT THE UNION PACIFIC RAILWAY.

In 1836 the first public meeting to consider the project of a Pacific railway was called by John Plumbe, a civil engineer of Dubuque, Iowa.   Interest in a Pacific railway increased from this time.   The explorations of Fremont in 1842 and 1846 brought the attention of Congress, and A. C. Whitney was zealous and efficient in the cause from 1840 to 1850.   The first practical measure was Senator Salmon P. Chase's bill, making an appropriation for the explorations of different routes for a Pacific railway in 1853.   Numerous bills were introduced in Congress between 1852 and 1860, granting subsidies and lands, and some of them appropriating as large a sum as $96,000,000 for the construction of the road.   One of these bills passed one of the houses of Congress.   The results of the explorations ordered by Congress were printed in eleven large volumes, covering the country between the parallels of latitude thirty-second on the south and forty-ninth on the north, and demonstrating the feasibility of building a Pacific railway, but at a cost on any one of the lines much larger than the Union Pacific and Central Pacific were built for.   It is a singular fact that in all these explorations the most feasible line in an engineering and commercial point of view, the line with the least obstacles to overcome, of lowest grades and least curvature, was never explored and reported on.   Private enterprise explored and developed that line along the forty-second parallel of latitude.

This route was made by the buffalo, next used by the Indians, then by the fur traders, next by the Mormons, and then by the overland immigration to California and Oregon.   It was known as the Great Platte Valley Route.   On this trail, or close to it, was built the Union and Central Pacific railroads to California, and the Oregon Short Line branch of the Union Pacific to Oregon.

In 1852 the Mississippi and Missouri Railroad Company was organized to build a line westward across the State of Iowa as an extension of the Chicago and Rock Island, then terminating at Rock Island, Ill.   The principal men connected with this line were Henry Farnum and Thomas C. Durant.   Peter A. Dey, who had been a division engineer of the Rock Island, was the chief engineer of the M. & M. in Iowa.   He was a man of great ability, probity, and integrity.

5

How We Built The Union Pacific.

In May, 1853, Mr. Peter A. Dey left the Rock Island, of which he was a division engineer, stationed at Tiskilwa, and commenced at Davenport, Iowa, the first survey of a railroad line across the State of Iowa. I had been with Mr. Dey about eight months as rodman, and under his direction had made a survey of the Peoria and Bureau Valley Railway in Illinois. Mr. Dey was made chief engineer of the M. & M., and took me to Iowa as assistant, and placed me in charge of the party in the field, certainly a very fine promotion for the limited experience I had, and it is one of the greatest satisfactions and pleasures of my life to have had his friendship from the time I entered his service until now. Mr. Dey is not only a very distinguished citizen of Iowa, but is one of the most eminent engineers of the country. He was known for his great ability, his uprightness, and the square deal he gave every one, and he has greatly honored his State in the many public positions he has held. I look back upon my services with him with the greatest pleasure. He has a wide reputation as a civil engineer and railway constructor, and in later years as railway commissioner for the State of Iowa.

In 1853 he gave the orders for the party that surveyed the first line across Iowa to examine the country west of the Missouri River. This was to determine where the M. & M. (now the Rock Island) line crossing Iowa should terminate on the Missouri River, in order to take advantage of, and, perhaps, become a part of the prospective line running west up the Great Platte Valley, then the chief thoroughfare for all the Mormon, California, and Oregon overland immigration. It fell to my lot to be chief of this party. My examinations virtually determined that a railway line extending west from the Missouri River should go by way of Sarpys Point (now Bellevue), or directly west from Kanesville, afterwards Council Bluffs, where the Mormons from Nauvoo were then resting on their way to Salt Lake.

My party crossed the Missouri River in the fall of 1853 on flatboats. The Omaha Indians occupied the country where we landed, and after obtaining a line rising from the bluffs west of where the city of Omaha now stands, I gave directions to the party to continue the survey while I went on ahead to examine the country to the Platte Valley some 25 miles farther west. I reached the Platte Valley about noon the next day, and being very tired, I lariated my horse and laid down with my saddle as a pillow and with my rifle under it, and went sound asleep. I was awakened by the neighing of the horse, and when I looked up I saw an Indian leading the horse toward the Elkhorn River, pulling with all his might and the horse holding back, evidently frightened. I was greatly frightened myself, hardly knowing what to do, but I suppose from instinct I grabbed my rifle

6

and started after the Indian, hollering at the top of my voice. The Indian saw me coming, let the horse go, and made his way across the Elkhorn River. This Indian afterwards was an enlisted man in the battalion of Pawnees that served under me in the Indian campaigns of 1865, and he told Major North, the commander of that battalion, that he let loose of the horse because I hollered so loud that it frightened him. On obtaining my horse, I saddled up and made my way back to the party that was camped on the Big Papillion on the emigrant road leading from Florence to the Elkhorn. The camp was full of Omaha Indians and they had every man in the party cooking for them. I saw that we would soon lose all our provisions, and as the party was armed, I called them together and told them to get their arms. I only knew one Indian word, " Puckechee," which meant get out. That I told them, and while the Indians were surly they saw we were determined and they left us. I don't believe there was anyone in the party that had ever seen an Indian before or had any experience with them. We were all tenderfeet. It taught me a lesson, never to allow an Indian in my camp or around it without permission, and this was my instructions to all our engineering parties. Those who obeyed it generally got through without losing their stock or lives. Those who were careless and disobeyed generally lost their stock and some of their men. As soon as we had determined the line from the Missouri River to the Platte we returned to Iowa City, which was the headquarters of the M. & M. Railway.

The times were such that the work on the M. & M. Railway was suspended for some years. Meanwhile I located at Council Bluffs, continuing the explorations under the direction of Messrs. Farnam and Durant, and obtaining from voyagers, immigrants, and others all the information I could in regard to the country farther west. There was keen competition at that time for the control of the vast immigration crossing the plains, and Kansas City, Fort Leavenworth (then the government post), St. Joseph, and Council Bluffs were points of concentration on the Missouri. The trails from all the points converged in the Platte Valley at or near old Fort Kearney, following its waters to the South Pass. A portion of the Kansas City immigration followed the valley of the Arkansas west, and thence through New Mexico. The great bulk of the immigration was finally concentrated at Council Bluffs as the best crossing of the Missouri River. From my explorations and the information I had obtained with the aid of the Mormons and others, I mapped and made an itinerary of a line from Council Bluffs through to Utah, California, and Oregon, giving the camping places for each night, and showing where wood, water, and fords of streams could be found. Distributed broadcast by the local interests of this route this map

7

and itinerary had no small influence in turning the mass of overland immigration to Council Bluffs, where it crossed the Missouri and took the great Platte Valley route. This route was up that valley to its forks, and then up either the north or south fork to Salt Lake and California by way of the Humboldt, and to Oregon by way of the Snake and Columbia rivers. This is to-day the route of the Union and Central Pacifics to California and the Union Pacific to Oregon.

After collecting all the information we could as to the best route for a railroad to the Pacific, I reported to Messrs. Farnam and Durant, who paid out of their private funds for all my work. In 1857 or 1858 they asked me to visit New York. In the office of the Rock Island Railroad, over the Corn Exchange Bank in William street, I was brought before the board of directors of that road and the Mississippi and Missouri Railway, together with some friends who had been called in. The secretary of the company read my report. Before he was half through nearly every person had left the room, and when he had finished only Mr. Farnam, Mr. Durant, the reader, and myself were present. I could see that there was lack of faith and even interest in the matter. One of the directors said in the outer room that he did not see why they should be asked to hear such nonsense, but Messrs. Farnam and Durant did not lose faith. Since our survey in 1853, other companies had made surveys in Iowa, all concentrating at Council Bluffs. Farnam and Durant felt that if they could stimulate interest in the Pacific road it would enable them to raise funds to complete their line across the State, and authority was conferred upon me to begin work at Council Bluffs and build east through Pottawattamie County, if I could obtain local aid. This we secured, and the road was graded through that county, when we were called east to continue the work from Iowa City west.

In 1854, when Nebraska was organized, we moved to its frontier, continuing the explorations under the patronage of Messrs. Farnam and Durant, and obtaining all valuable information, which was used to concentrate the influence of the different railways east and west of Chicago to the support of the forty-second parallel line.

In 1861 we discontinued the railroad work because of the civil war. The passage of the bill of 1862, which made the building of a transcontinental railroad possible, was due primarily to the persistent efforts of Hon. Samuel R. Curtis, a Representative in Congress from Iowa, who reported the bill before entering the Union service in 1861. It was then taken up by Hon. James Harlan, of Iowa, who succeeded in obtaining its passage in March, 1862.

Up to 1858 all the projects for building a railroad across the continent were regarded as the Pacific roads, each route mentioned having a particular name. The line along the forty-second parallel of latitude was designated as a line from San Francisco to a point on the Missouri River not farther north than Council Bluffs and not farther south than Independence, Mo., and was called the Pacific Railroad. The line surveyed by Stephens along the forty-ninth parallel of latitude was called the North Route. The route along the thirty-eighth and thirty-ninth parallels, as the Buffalo Trail. It received that name from Thomas H. Benton. The route along the thirty-fifth and thirty-second parallels, as the South Route. The Government, however, made no explorations along the forty-second parallel; that was done by individual enterprise. In 1856 both political parties in convention passed resolutions favoring a Pacific railroad, and in 1857 President Buchanan advocated it as a reason for holding the Pacific coast people in the Union, and it was this sentiment that gave to the forty-second parallel line the name of the Union Pacific Railroad. In 1858 a select committee of fifteen was authorized by Congress on Pacific railroads and in the Thirty-fifth Congress, second session, this committee allowed the Hon. Samuel R. Curtis, of Iowa, to report the bill, and if I recollect rightly, this was the first bill that took the name of Union Pacific. In the Thirty-sixth Congress General Curtis became the champion of the Union Pacific Railroad, and it was advocated then as a strong element in holding the Union together. Curtis's bill passed the House in December, 1860. It failed to become a law, as the question of secession was up then and Lincoln had been elected President. In the extra session of the Thirty-second Congress in July, 1861, Curtis reintroduced the bill and he left Congress to enter the army. When Representative Campbell, of Pennsylvania, became chairman of the committee, Senator Harlan, of Iowa, who had been elected to the Senate, became the strongest advocate of the bill in the Senate. Lincoln advocated its passage and building, not only as a military necessity, but as a means of holding the Pacific coast to the Union. This bill became a law in 1862, and there is no doubt but what the sentiment that the building of the railroad would hold the Union together gave it the name of the Union Pacific.

The Union Pacific Railway was organized on September 2, 1862, at Chicago, Maj. Gen. S. R. Curtis, of Iowa, being chairman of the commissioners appointed by Congress. The organization was perfected by making Henry B. Ogden, of Chicago, president; Thomas W. Olcott, treasurer, and Henry V. Poor, secretary. Mr. T. C. Durant selected Peter A. Dey to make a reconnoissance from the Missouri River to Salt Lake to be reported at the next meeting of the board. Mr. Dey immediately entered upon his work and extended his reconnoissance through to Salt Lake Valley.

In the spring of 1863, when in command of the district of Corinth, Miss., I received a dispatch from General Grant to proceed to Washington and report to President Lincoln. No explanation coming with the dispatch, and having a short time before organized and armed some negroes for the purpose of guarding a contraband camp which we had at Corinth, which act had been greatly criticised in the army and by civilians, I was somewhat alarmed, thinking possibly I was to be called to account. But on arriving at Washington I discovered that my summons was due to an interview between Mr. Lincoln and myself at Council Bluffs in August, 1859. He was there to look after an interest in the Riddle tract he had bought of Mr. N. B. Judd, of Chicago. I had just arrived from an exploring trip to the westward. It was quite an event for an exploring party to reach the States, and after dinner, while I was resting on the stoop of the Pacific House, Mr. Lincoln sat down beside me, and by his kindly ways soon drew from me all I knew of the country west, and the results of my reconnaissances. As the saying is, he completely " shelled my woods," getting all the secrets that were later to go to my employers.

Under the law of 1862 the President was to fix the eastern terminus of the Union Pacific Railway, and, remembering our talk in the fifties, he wished to consult me in the matter. Several towns on the Missouri River were competing for the terminus, but Mr. Lincoln practically settled the question in favor of the location I recommended. He issued his first order on November 17, 1863. It was in his own language, and as follows:

I, Abraham Lincoln, President of the United States, do hereby fix so much of the western boundary of the State of Iowa as lies between the north and south boundaries of the United States township within which the city of Omaha is situated as the point from which the line of railroad and telegraph in that section mentioned shall be constructed.

This order was not considered definite enough by the company, and on March 7, 1864, President Lincoln issued the second executive order, as follows:

I, Abraham Lincoln, President of the United States, do, upon the application of said company, designate and establish such first-named point on the eastern boundary of the State of Iowa east of and opposite to the east line of section 10, in township 15 south, of range 13 east, of the sixth principal meridian in the Territory of Nebraska.

On March 8, 1864, he notified the United States Senate that on the 17th day of November, 1863, he had located the " eastern terminus of the Union Pacific Railway within the limits of the township in Iowa opposite to the town of Omaha." Since then, he says, the company has represented to me that upon additional survey made it has determined upon the precise point of departure of the branch road from the Missouri River, and located same within the limits designated in the order of November last.

He was very anxious that the road should be built and discussed that question with me.

I explained to him as clearly as I could how difficult it would be to build it by private enterprise, and said I thought it should be taken up and built by the Government. He objected to this, saying the Government would give the project all possible aid and support, but could not build the road; that it had all it could possibly handle in the conflict now going on. But the Government would make any change in the law or give any reasonable aid to insure the building of the road by private enterprise.

After my interview with the President, I proceeded to New York and met Mr. T. C. Durant, then practically at the head of the Union Pacific interests, and other interested persons. After I had presented the President's views they took new courage, and at the yearly meeting of the company, Gen. John A. Dix was made president, Thomas C. Durant, vice-president, H. V. Poor, secretary, and J. J. Cisco, treasurer. They then submitted to Congress the necessary changes needed in the law of 1862, in order to bring the capital of the country to their support.

In the fall of 1863 Mr. Durant had personally instructed Mr. Dey to organize parties for immediate surveys to determine the line from the Missouri River up the Platte Valley, to run a line over the first range of mountains, known as the Black Hills, and to examine the Wasatch Range. In his report Mr. Durant said:

It is here that the information derived from the examinations made by Gen. G. M. Dodge, and those made last year by Peter A. Dey, who was sent out by the committee appointed by your board of commissioners, proved of great value, as the present parties will avail themselves of the examinations made by these gentlemen, and will first run the lines which they found most practicable.

In accordance with these instructions, Mr. Dey placed B. B. Brayton in charge of the party examining the Black Hills, and, at Mr. Dey's request, Brigham Young placed his son, James A. Young, in charge of the surveys over the Wasatch. Mr. Dey, who had become chief engineer, placed engineering parties in the field covering the territory from the Missouri River to Salt Lake.

Ground was broken at Omaha for the beginning of the road on the 1st day of December, 1863, and after the passage of the act of 1864 about $500,000 was spent in grading and surveys.

A question as to the location brought a disturbing contest between Omaha and the company. Mr. Dey had located the line due west to the Elkhorn River. The consulting engineer, Colonel Seymour, recommended a change, increasing the distance 9 or more miles in 13.

The main argument for adding 9 miles of distance in 13 miles of road was that it eliminated the 80 and 66 foot grades of the direct line. If this had been done there would have been some argument for the change, but they only eliminated the grades from the Omaha summit west, while it took 3 miles of 60 and 66-foot grade from the Missouri River to reach this summit, and coming east the Elkhorn summit was an 80-foot grade, so by the change and addition of 9 miles they made no reductions in the original maximum grades, or in the tonnage hauled in a train on the new lines over the old line, if it had been built. The grades at Omaha and Elkhorn have been eliminated since 1900, and the new management are adopting the old Dey line for the distance it saves, and bringing the grade to the road's maximum of 47 feet to the mile. It was Mr. Dey's intention that when traffic demanded the original short line grades would be reduced to whatever maximum grade the road should finally adopt. After a long contest and many reports the Government provided that the change should only be made if the Omaha and Elkhorn grades were eliminated, the first by a line running south from Omaha 2 miles down the Missouri Valley and cutting through the bluffs to Muddy Creek, giving a 35-foot maximum grade, and the Elkhorn by additional cutting and filling without changing the line, but this was never done. The company paid no attention to the decision, but built on the changed line, letting the grades at Omaha and Elkhorn stand, and the government commissioners accepted the road, ignoring the Government's conditions for the change, and bonds were issued upon it, although it was a direct violation of the government order. The final decision in favor of the change and the ignoring of Mr. Dey's recommendations in letting the construction contracts caused Mr. Dey, in January, 1865, to send in his resignation. He stated in his letter of resignation that he was giving up " the best position in his profession this country has offered to any man."

The officers of the Union Pacific then requested me to return and take charge of the work. I was then in command of the United States forces on the plains in the Indian campaigns, and General Grant was not willing that I should leave, so I finished my work there and went to Omaha on the 1st of May, 1866, and assumed the duties of chief engineer, having been allowed leave of absence through the following letter of General Sherman:

HEADQUARTERS MILITARY DIVISION OF THE MISSISSIPPI,
St. Louis, May 1, 1866.

Major-General DODGE.

DEAR GENERAL: I have your letter of April 27, and I readily consent to what you ask. I think General Pope should be at Leavenworth before you leave, and I expected he would be at Leavenworth by May 1, but he has not yet come. As soon as he reaches Leavenworth, or St. Louis even, I consent to your going to Omaha to begin what, I trust, will be the real beginning of the great road. I start to-morrow for Riley, whence I will cross over to Kearney by land, and thence come in to Omaha, where I hope to meet you. I will send your letter this morning to Pope's office and indorse your request that a telegraph message be sent to General Pope to the effect that he is wanted at Leavenworth. Hoping to meet you soon, I am,

Yours, truly,

W. T. SHERMAN, *M. G.*

The organization for work on the plains away from civilization was as follows: Each of our surveying parties consisted of a chief, who was an experienced engineer, two assistants, also civil engineers, rodmen, flagmen, and chainmen, generally graduated civil engineers but without personal experience in the field, besides axmen, teamsters, and herders. When the party was expected to live upon the game of the country a hunter was added. Each party would thus consist of from eighteen to twenty-two men, all armed. When operating in a hostile Indian country they were regularly drilled, though after the civil war this was unnecessary, as most of them had been in the army. Each party entering a country occupied by hostile Indians was generally furnished with a military escort of from ten men to a company under a competent officer. The duty of this escort was to protect the party when in camp. In the field the escort usually occupied prominent hills commanding the territory in which the work was to be done, so as to head off sudden attacks by the Indians. Notwithstanding this protection, the parties were often attacked, their chief or some of their men killed or wounded, and their stock run off.

In preliminary surveys in the open country a party would run from 8 to 12 miles of line in a day. On location in an open country 3 or 4 miles would be covered, but in a mountainous country generally not to exceed a mile. All hands worked from daylight to dark, the country being reconnoitered ahead of them by the chief, who indicated the streams to follow, and the controlling points in summits and river crossings. The party of location that followed the preliminary surveys had the maps and profiles of the line selected for location and devoted its energies to obtaining a line of the lowest grades and the least curvature that the country would admit.

The location party in our work on the Union Pacific was followed by the construction corps, grading generally 100 miles at a time. That distance was graded in about thirty days on the plains, as a rule, but in the mountains we sometimes had to open our grading several hundred miles ahead of our track in order to complete the grading by the time the track should reach it. All the supplies for this work had to be hauled from the end of the track, and the wagon transportation was enormous. At one time we were using at least

13

10,000 animals, and most of the time from 8,000 to 10,000 laborers. The bridge gangs always worked from 5 to 20 miles ahead of the track, and it was seldom that the track waited for a bridge. To supply 1 mile of track with material and supplies required about 40 cars, as on the plains everything, rails, ties, bridging, fastenings, all railway supplies, fuel for locomotives and trains, and supplies for men and animals on the entire work, had to be transported from the Missouri River. Therefore, as we moved westward, every hundred miles added vastly to our transportation. Yet the work was so systematically planned and executed that I do not remember an instance in all the construction of the line of the work being delayed a single week for want of material. Each winter we planned the work for the next season. By the opening of spring, about April 1, every part of the machinery was in working order, and in no year did we fail to accomplish our work. After 1866 the reports will show what we started out to do each year, and what we accomplished.

The following extract from a letter written to me by Gen. W. T. Sherman as to what we promised to do in 1867, which was only about one-half what we prepared to do and did accomplish in 1868, indicates how one year's experience helped us in the progress of the next. It also shows, what the country now seems in a great measure to have forgotten, that the Pacific Railroad, now regarded chiefly in the light of a transcontinental, commercial highway, was then looked upon as a military necessity and as the one thing positively essential to the binding together of the republic East and West:

ST. LOUIS, *January 16, 1867.*

MY DEAR DODGE: I have just read with intense interest your letter of the 14th, and, though you wanted it kept to myself, I believe you will sanction my sending it to General Grant for his individual perusal, to be returned to me. It is almost a miracle to grasp your purpose to finish to Fort Sanders (288 miles) this year, but you have done so much that I mistrust my own judgment and accept yours. I regard this road of yours as the solution of the Indian affairs and the Mormon question, and, therefore, give you all the aid I possibly can, but the demand for soldiers everywhere and the slowness of enlistment, especially among the blacks, limit our ability to respond. Each officer exaggerates his own troubles and appeals for men. I now have General Terry on the upper Missouri, General Augur with you, and General Hancock just below, all enterprising young men, fit for counsel or for the field. I will endeavor to arrange so that hereafter all shall act on common principles and with a common purpose, and the first step, of course, is to arrange for the accumulation of the necessary men and materials at the right points, for which your railroad is the very thing. So far as interest in your section is concerned, you may rest easy that both Grant and I feel deeply concerned in the safety of your great national enterprise.

It was not until after November, 1867, when we had been at work two years, that we got railroad communication with the East at Coun-

DALE CREEK BRIDGE.

Main line, Union Pacific Railway.

cil Bluffs, Iowa, the initial point of the Union Pacific Railway, by the completion of the Northwestern Railway. Till then the Missouri River had been the sole route over which supplies could be had. It was available only about three months of the year, and our construction was limited by the quantities of rail and equipment that could be brought to us by boat in that time. In twelve months of work after we had rail communication, we located, built, and equipped 587 miles of road, working only from one end, transporting everything connected with it an average distance of 800 miles west of the Missouri River. This feat has not yet been surpassed. In accomplishing it we crossed the divide of the continent and two ranges of mountains, one of which was the Wasatch, where in the winter of 1868–69 we had to blast the earth the same as the rocks.

Our Indian troubles commenced in 1864 and lasted until the tracks joined at Promontory. We lost most of our men and stock while building from Fort Kearney to Bitter Creek. At that time every mile of road had to be surveyed, graded, tied, and bridged under military protection. The order to every surveying corps, grading, bridging, and tie outfit was never to run when attacked. All were required to be armed, and I do not know that the order was disobeyed in a single instance, nor did I ever hear that the Indians had driven a party permanently from its work. I remember one occasion when they swooped down on a grading outfit in sight of the temporary fort of the military some 5 miles away, and right in sight of the end of the track. The government commission to examine that section of the completed road had just arrived, and the commissioners witnessed the fight. The graders had their arms stacked on the cut. The Indians leaped from the ravines, and, springing upon the workmen before they could reach their arms, cut loose the stock and caused a panic. Gen. Frank P. Blair, General Simpson, and Doctor White were the commissioners, and they showed their grit by running to my car for arms to aid in the fight. We did not fail to benefit from this experience, for, on returning to the East the commission dwelt earnestly on the necessity of our being protected.

From the beginning to the completion of the road our success depended in a great measure on the cordial and active support of the army, especially its commander in chief, General Grant, and the commander of the Military Division of the West, General Sherman. He took a personal interest in the project. He visited the work several times each year during its continuance, and I was in the habit of communicating with him each month, detailing my progress and laying before him my plans. In return I received letters from him almost every month. We also had the cordial support of the district commanders of the country through which we operated—General

Augur, General Cook, General Gibbon, and General Stevenson, and their subordinates. General Grant had given full and positive instructions that every support should be given to me, and General Sherman in the detailed instructions practically left it to my own judgment as to what support should be given by the troops on the plains. They were also instructed to furnish my surveying parties with provisions from the posts whenever our provisions should give out, and the subordinate officers, following the example of their chiefs, responded to every demand made, no matter at what time of day or night, what time of year or in what weather, and took as much interest in the matter as we did.

General Sherman's great interest in the enterprise originated from the fact that he personally, in 1849, took from General Smith, commander on the Pacific coast, the instructions to Lieutenants Warner and Williamson, of the engineers, who made the first surveys coming east from California, to ascertain, if possible, whether it was practicable to cross the Sierra Nevada range of mountains with a railroad. These instructions were sent at General Sherman's own suggestion, and the orders and examination preceded the act of Congress making appropriations for explorations and surveys for a railroad route from the Mississippi River to the Pacific Ocean by four years. General Sherman's interest lasted during his lifetime, and was signalized in the closing days of his official life by a summary of transcontinental railroad construction, the most exhaustive paper on the subject I have ever seen.

When I took charge as chief engineer of the Union Pacific Railway in 1866, I knew that my first duty would be to determine the crossing of the line over the Black Hills, a bold, high spur of the Rocky Mountains, and I concentrated my engineering forces for that purpose. It had already been ascertained that we could get down to the Laramie plains from the summit going west, but the route had not been determined going east. In my examinations made while coming home from the Powder River expedition in 1865 I had found what I believed to be the most practicable route from the summit to the foot of the mountains on the east, and directed that it be examined. This was immediately done, and the route was found practicable.

After the battle of Atlanta, my assignment to the Department of the Missouri brought the country between the Missouri River and California under my command, and then I was charged with the Indian campaigns of 1865 and 1866. I traveled again over all that portion of the country I had explored in former years, and saw the beginning of that great future that awaited it. I then began to comprehend its capabilities and resources; and in all movements of our troops and scouting parties I had reports made upon the country—its resources and topography; and I, myself, during the two years traversed it east and west, north and south, from the Arkansas to the Yellowstone, and from the Missouri to Salt Lake basin.

It was on one of these trips that I discovered the pass through the Black Hills and gave it the name of Sherman, in honor of my great chief. Its elevation is 8,236 feet, and for years it was the highest point reached by any railroad in the United States. The circumstances of this accidental discovery may not be uninteresting.

While returning from the Powder River campaign, I was in the habit of leaving my troops and trains, and with a few men, examining all the approaches and passes from Fort Laramie south over the secondary range of mountains known as the Black Hills, the most difficult to overcome with proper grades of all the ranges, on account of its short slopes and great height. When I reached the Lodge Pole Creek, up which went the overland trail, I took a few mounted men— I think six—and with one of my scouts as guide, went up the creek to the summit of Cheyenne Pass, striking south along the crest of the mountains to obtain a good view of the country, the troops and trains at the same time passing along the east base of the mountains on what was known as the St. Vrain and the Laramie trail.

About noon, in the valley of a tributary of Crow Creek, we discovered Indians, who, at the same time, discovered us. They were between us and our trains. I saw our danger and took means immediately to reach the ridge and try to head them off, and follow it to where the cavalry could see our signals. We dismounted and started down the ridge, holding the Indians at bay, when they came too near, with our Winchesters. It was nearly night when the troops saw our smoke signals of danger and came to our relief; and in going to the train we followed this ridge out until I discovered it led down to the plains without a break. I then said to my guide that if we saved our scalps I believed we had found the crossing of the Black Hills—and over this ridge, between Lone Tree and Crow creeks, the wonderful line over the mountains was built. For over two years all explorations had failed to find a satisfactory crossing of this range. The country east of it was unexplored, but we had no doubt we could reach it.

The year 1866 was spent in determining the crossing of the Rocky Mountains or the Black Hills, and the approaches to them from the east. It was the great desire of the company to build the line through Denver, Colo., if possible, up the South Platte Valley and crossing the mountains west of Denver and reaching Salt Lake by the Yampa, White, and Uinta valleys, and I covered the country from the Laramie Canyon on the north to the Arkansas on the south, examining all the mountain passes and approaches and examined all these lines personally. These surveys demonstrated that there was no question as to where the line should cross these mountains. The general examination of the plains along the east foot of the mountains showed that the plains rose from the Arkansas north until they reached their apex at the valley of Crow Creek, near where Cheyenne now stands. Then they fell to the north toward the Laramie, and when we came to examine the summits of these mountains, we found their lowest altitude was in the vicinity of the Cheyenne Pass, so that there was no question as to where our line should run. The line up the Platte and up the Lodge Pole and by the Lone Tree Pass which I had discovered, was far superior to any other line, and it forced us to abandon the line in the direction of Denver, and we had in view the building of a branch from Crow Creek to Denver, about 112 miles long. I reported the result of my examination on November 15, 1866, to the company, and on November 23, 1866, the company adopted the lines which I had recommended, and I immediately proceeded to develop them for building the next year. We also examined this year the line by the way of the North Platte, Fort Laramie, Sweet Water Creek and the South Pass, reaching Salt Lake by the way of the Big Sandy and Black Fork. This line avoided the crossing of the Black Hills and the heavy grade ascending from the east to the summit and the ninety-foot grade dropping down into the Laramie plains, but this line was some forty miles longer than the direct line by the Lodge Pole, and on this line there was no development of coal as there was on the line adopted by the company, and on presenting this question to the Government, they decided against the North Platte and South Pass line. The chiefs of parties for this work were: James A. Evans, who was an engineer of great ability, Mr. P. T. Brown, who was an assistant engineer, a young man who started out in 1864 as a rodman. He made the surveys through Clear Creek to the Middle Park, over the Burthud Pass; also the Boulder Pass. On this pass in November, the party was caught in the severest snow storm known in the mountains, and he was obliged to abandon his pack train and save his party by working his way eastward through the storm to Boulder Creek. His stock drifted to Middle Park. There they wintered near the hot springs. I received knowledge through one of my old mountain friends that they were there in good condition, and we recovered them in the spring. Mr. L. L. Hills, assistant engineer, had charge of the surveys on the Lodge Pole line and up the Cache La Poudre River to Laramie Plains, and Mr. J. E. House had charge of the surveys, soundings, and examination of the Missouri River. Mr. F. A. Case, division engineer, was completing the examination of the passes through the main range, made the year before, and Mr. F. H. Ainsworth was running the lines in the Platte Valley, while Mr. Thomas H. Bates had charge of the surveys in Utah and west to the California state line. The explorations and surveys of 1866 had only confirmed the reconnoissance made in the fifties by Mr. Dey and myself of the general route of the Union Pacific Railroad, so that for the years to come our work would be almost entirely devoted to the final locations.

In the spring of 1867 I received a letter from General Grant, suggesting that in my explorations during the year 1867, I take with me his chief of staff, Gen. John A. Rawlins, for the benefit of his health. General Rawlins had shown a tendency toward consumption, and it was thought that three or four months in camp on the plains would be of great benefit to him. I therefore with great pleasure invited General Rawlins to accompany me, with such friends as he might select. He came to me at Omaha, bringing with him Maj. J. W. McK. Dunn, A. D. C., and John E. Corwith, of Galena, Ill., and added to this party on my invitation was John R. Duff, son of a director of the road, and Mr. David Van Lennep, my geologist. We had as an escort two companies of cavalry and two of infantry, under the command of Lieut. Col. J. K. Mizner, who had with him Lieut. J. W. Wheelan and Dr. Henry B. Terry, assistant surgeon, U. S. Army. They accompanied me during the entire summer. We started out the 1st of June and went to the end of the track, which was then at North Platte, and from there we marched immediately up the Platte, then up the Lodge Pole to the east base of the Black Hills, where we were joined by Gen C. C. Augur, who was then in command of that department, with his staff. General Augur's instructions were to locate the military post where I located the end of the division, at the east base of the mountains, and after a thorough examination of the country, I located the division point on Crow Creek, where Cheyenne now stands, and named it Cheyenne, and General Augur immediately located just north of the town the military post of D. A. Russell. We spent the Fourth of July at this place, and Gen. John A. Rawlins delivered a very remarkable and patriotic speech.

At this time the heaviest settlement was Denver, some 112 miles away. While we were camped here the Indians swooped down out of the ravine of Crow Creek and attacked a Mormon grading train and outfit that was coming from Salt Lake to take work on the road and killed two if its men. Our cavalry hastily mounted and drove off the Indians and saved their stock. We buried the men and started the graveyard of the future city, now the capital of the State of Wyoming.

How We Built The Union Pacific.

In the spring of 1867 there was a party in the field under L. L. Hills running a line east from the base of the Rocky Mountains. The first word I received from it was through the commanding officer at Camp Collins, who had served under me while I commanded the department. He informed me that a young man named J. M. Eddy had brought the party into that post, its chief having been killed in a fight with the Indians. I inquired who Eddy was and was informed that he was an axman in the party, and had served under me in the civil war. I ordered him to meet me with his party on the Lodge Pole as I traveled west. He turned out to be a young boy who had entered the Thirteenth Illinois when only 16 or 17. The fight in which Mr. Hills, the chief, was killed occurred some 6 miles east of Cheyenne, and after the leader was lost young Eddy rallied the party and by the force of his own character took it into Camp Collins. Of course I immediately promoted him. He was with me during the entire construction of the Union Pacific, rising from one position to another, until he became the general manager of portions of the great Southwestern system. He died in the railway service.

After meeting this party, I completed the location of the line to Crow Creek, at the foot of the mountains, now known as Cheyenne.

We marched west across the Black Hills and Laramie Plains and passed through Rattle Snake Hills Pass, following down a stream that emptied into the Platte just opposite Fort Steele and at a point where the Union Pacific now crosses the North Platte River. We crossed this stream by swimming our horses and proceeded west. The country from the Platte west to the Bitter Creek is very dry, no running water in it, and before we reached camp General Rawlins became very thirsty, and we started out in an endeavor to find running water, and I discovered a spring in a draw near where the town of Rawlins now stands. When General Rawlins reached this spring he said it was the most gracious and acceptable of anything he had had on the march, and also said that if any thing was ever named for him, he wanted it to be a spring of water, and I said then, " We will name this Rawlins Springs." It took that name. The end of one of our divisions happened to be close to this spring, and I named the station Rawlins, which has grown now into quite a town and a division point of the Union Pacific road.

As soon as I had determined the line over the Black Hills, I learned that one of the parties which was trying to work west from the North Platte had found the maps of the country misleading. Endeavoring to find the summit of the continental divide, this party had dropped into a great basin. Percy T. Brown, the chief of the party, finding himself in an unknown country entirely different in character from what had been expected, took eight of his escort and

GENERAL G. M. DODGE AND PARTY OF EXPLORATION.

Left to right, standing: Lieut. J. W. Wheelan, Lieut. Col. J. K. Mizner, Dr. Henry B. Terry, John E. Corwith.
Left to right, sitting: D. Van Lennep, John R. Duff, Gen. G. M. Dodge, John A. Rawlins, J. W. McK. Dunn.

started to explore the region. When near the center of what is now known as the Red Desert he was attacked by 300 Sioux Indians working south to the Bridger Pass stage road coming from the Sweetwater. Brown took measures to defend himself, occupying, after a severe contest with the Indians for its possession, a small hill, and fighting from 12 o'clock noon until toward night, when he was shot through the abdomen. He then ordered the soldiers to leave him and save themselves, but they refused, and allowed the Indians to get hold of the stock, after which the redskins withdrew. The soldiers then made a litter of their carbines and packed Brown upon it 15 miles through the sagebrush to Laclere station, near Bridgers Pass. Their laborious efforts to save him were made in vain, however, for Brown died at the station.

Upon an examination of this country we discovered that the divide of the continent had let down from the Wind River Mountains on the north to Medicine Bow, the beginning of the main Rocky Mountains on the south from an elevation of 13,000 feet to one of 7,000 into an open plain, and that the divide was in reality a great basin about 80 miles across in its widest part east and west, and 100 to 150 miles northwest and southeast in its longest part. The streams running into it sink, leaving a red soil over the entire basin, from which it receives the name of the Red Desert. The Union Pacific Railway crossed the Red Desert near its southern limit, between the stations of Creston and Tipton, a distance of about 31 miles.

In the basin we found and rescued the party headed by Thomas F. Bates, which was coming from Green River east. When I reached what is now Creston I discovered Bates and his party. They had been in the widest part of the basin for nearly a week without water, and were almost exhausted. When we discovered them they had abandoned the line and were taking a course due east by the compass, running for water. At first we thought them Indians, but on looking through my glasses I saw that they had teams with them. We went to their relief at once and saved them. They were in a deplorable condition from thirst.

On the western rim of the basin, as I left it, I ran into the remains of some old wagons and other articles which indicated that some military force had tried to cross there. Afterwards I learned that it had been Colonel Steptoe's expedition to Oregon, and that in crossing from Bridgers Pass trying to reach northwest, they struck this country and were obliged to abandon a portion of their outfit. This demonstrated that no knowledge of this depression was had by anyone until we developed it in our surveys. We had great difficulty in obtaining water for the operation of our road through the basin, being obliged to sink artesian wells to a great depth. After reaching the west rim of the Red Desert you immediately drop into the valley of Bitter Creek, the waters of which flow into the Pacific. The crossing of the continental divide by the Union Pacific is thus by way of an open prairie of comparatively low elevation, about 7,000 feet, instead of a mountain range. The work of building the road there was unexpectedly light, and it almost seems that nature made this great opening in the Rocky Mountains expressly for the passage of a transcontinental railway.

The law of 1862 provided that the Union Pacific and Central Pacific should join their tracks at the California state line. The law of 1864 allowed the Central Pacific to build 150 miles east of the state line, but that was changed by the law of 1866, and the two companies allowed to build, one east and the other west, until they met. The building of 500 miles of road during the summers of 1866 and 1867, hardly twelve months' actual work, had aroused great interest in the country, and much excitement, in which the Government took a part. We were pressed to as speedy a completion of the road as possible, although ten years had been allowed by Congress. The officers of the Union Pacific had become imbued with this spirit, and they urged me to plan to build as much road as possible in 1868. I have already alluded to the completion of the Northwestern Railway in December, 1867, to Council Bluffs, Iowa, which gave us an all-rail connection with the East, so that we could obtain our rail material and equipment during the entire year. The reaching of the summit of the first range of the Rocky Mountains, which I named Sherman, in honor of my old commander, in 1867, placed us comparatively near good timber for ties and bridges, which, after cutting, could be floated down the mountain streams at some points to our crossing, and at others to within 25 or 30 miles of our work. This afforded great relief to the transportation.

In the fall of 1867, when we closed our work and ended our track at the summit of the Black Hills, the company was apparently at their end, so far as finances were concerned, and were greatly disturbed as to the future. When I had received all of my parties' reports, extending to the California state line, and had completed the profiles, maps, and estimates, I went on to New York and met the board of directors, and when they saw the very favorable line that we had obtained over the Black Hills, across the Laramie plains and over the divide of the continent, where they had expected to meet very heavy work, and also the line over the Wasatch Range to Salt Lake and from there on west, they were very much encouraged. The estimates on this line were not more than one-half of what they had expected, and then a few miles west of Cheyenne they would commence receiving $48,000 in government bonds per mile for 150 miles, and from there on $32,000 in government bonds per mile, which was a great advance on the amount that they had received on the 630 miles from the Missouri River to the east base of the mountains, which was only $16,000 in government bonds per mile, while the cost of the work had been very heavy on account of the long distance rails, timber, supplies, and everything had to be hauled and the extra cost from the fact that the country furnished nothing for the road. The company immediately made extraordinary effort to provide the money to build to Salt Lake, and during the winter I received instructions to make every effort to build as much line as possible the coming year, and the company forwarded to us at our base on the Missouri River an immense amount of rails, fastenings, etc., as we then had rail connections by the Northwestern road all the way to Council Bluffs.

We made our plans to build to Salt Lake, 480 miles, in 1868, and to endeavor to meet the Central Pacific at Humboldt Wells, 219 miles west of Ogden, in the spring of 1869. I had extended our surveys during the years 1867 and 1868 to the California state line, and laid my plans before the company, and the necessary preparations were made to commence work as soon as frost was out of the ground, say about April 1. Material had been collected in sufficient quantities at the end of the track to prevent any delay. During the winter ties and bridge timber had been cut and prepared in the mountains to bring to the line at convenient points, and the engineering forces were started to their positions before cold weather was over, that they might be ready to begin their work as soon as the temperature would permit. I remember that the parties going to Salt Lake crossed the Wasatch Mountains on sledges, and that the snow covered the tops of the telegraph poles. We all knew and appreciated that the task we had laid out would require the greatest energy on the part of all hands. About April 1, therefore, I went onto the plains myself and started our construction forces, remaining the whole summer between Laramie and the Humboldt Mountains. I was surprised at the rapidity with which the work was carried forward. Winter caught us in the Wasatch Mountains, but we kept on grading our road and laying our track in the snow and ice at a tremendous cost. I estimated for the company that the extra cost of thus forcing the work during that summer and winter was over $10,000,000, but the instructions I received were to go on, no matter what the cost. Spring found us with the track at Ogden, and by May 1 we had reached Promontory, 534 miles west of our starting point twelve months before. Work on our line was opened to Humboldt Wells, making in the year a grading of 754 miles of line.

The Central Pacific had made wonderful progress coming east, and we abandoned the work from Promontory to Humboldt Wells, bending all our efforts to meet them at Promontory. Between Ogden and Promontory each company graded a line, running side by side, and in some places one line was right above the other. The laborers upon the Central Pacific were Chinamer, while ours were Irishmen, and there was much ill-feeling between them. Our Irishmen were in the habit of firing their blasts in the cuts without giving warning to the Chinamen on the Central Pacific working right above them. From this cause several Chinamen were severely hurt. Complaint was made to me by the Central Pacific people, and I endeavored to have the contractors bring all hostilities to a close, but, for some reason or other, they failed to do so. One day the Chinamen, appreciating the situation, put in what is called a " grave " on their work, and when the Irishmen right under them were all at work let go their blast and buried several of our men. This brought about a truce at once. From that time the Irish laborers showed due respect for the Chinamen, and there was no further trouble.

When the two roads approached in May, 1869, we agreed to connect at the summit of Promontory Point, and the day was fixed so that trains could reach us from New York and California. We laid the rails to the junction point a day or two before the final closing. Coming from the East, representing the Union Pacific, were Thomas C. Durant, vice-president; Sidney Dillon, who had taken a prominent part in the construction of the road from the beginning, and John R. Duff, directors, together with the consulting engineer and a carload of friends. From the West the representatives of the Central Pacific were its president, Leland Stanford; Mr. Collis P. Huntington, Mr. Crocker, Mr. Hopkins, Mr. Colton, and other members of that company, and Mr. Montague, chief engineer, and a detachment of troops from Camp Douglass, Salt Lake City. The two trains pulled up facing each other, each crowded with workmen who sought advantageous positions to witness the ceremonies, and literally covered the cars. The officers and invited guests formed on each side of the track, leaving it open to the south. The telegraph lines had been brought to that point, so that in the final spiking as each blow was struck the telegraph recorded it at each connected office from the Atlantic to the Pacific. Prayer was offered, a number of spikes were driven in the two adjoining rails, each one of the prominent persons present taking a hand, but very few hitting the spikes, to the great amusement of the crowd. When the last spike was placed, light taps were given upon it by several officials, and it was finally driven home by the chief engineer of the Union Pacific Railway. The engineers ran up their locomotives until they touched, the engineer upon each

24

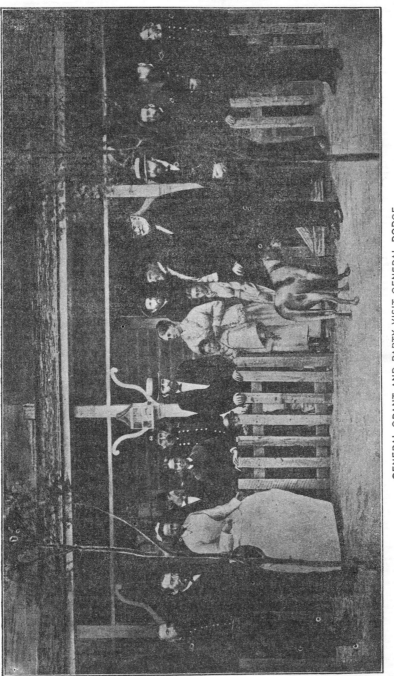

GENERAL GRANT AND PARTY VISIT GENERAL DODGE.

Summer of 1868, Fort Sanders, Wyoming.

From left to right: Gen. August Kautz, Gen. Philip H. Sheridan, Mrs. Potter, Gen. Frederick Dent, Mrs. Sheridan, Mrs. Gibbon, Gen. John Gibbon, Master John Gibbon, Gen. U. S. Grant, Katie Gibbon, Mrs. Kilburn, Allie Porter, Gen. G. M. Dodge, Lieut. Gen. Wm. T. Sherman, Gen. Wm. S. Harney, Dr. T. C. Durant, Gen. Adam Slemmer, Gen. Joseph C. Potter, Gen. Louis C. Hunt.

engine breaking a bottle of champagne upon the other one, and thus the two roads were wedded into one great trunk line from the Atlantic to the Pacific. Spikes of silver and gold were brought specially for the occasion, and later were manufactured into miniature spikes as mementos of the occasion. It was a bright but cold day. After a few speeches we all took refuge in the Central Pacific cars, where wine flowed freely, and many speeches were made.

Telegrams were sent to President Grant, Vice-President Colfax, and other officials throughout the country. I did not fail to send a message to my old commander, who had been such a helpful factor in the building of the road, and I received this message in response:

WASHINGTON, *May 11, 1869.*

Gen. G. M. DODGE: In common with millions, I sat yesterday and heard the mystic taps of the telegraph battery announce the nailing of the last spike in the great Pacific road. Indeed, am I its friend? Yea, Yet, am I to be a part of it, for as early as 1854 I was vice-president of the effort begun in San Francisco under the contract of Robinson, Seymour & Co. As soon as General Thomas makes certain preliminary inspections in his new command on the Pacific, I will go out, and, I need not say, will have different facilities from that of 1846, when the only way to California was by sail around Cape Horn, taking our ships 196 days. All honor to you, to Durant, to Jack and Dan Casement, to Reed, and the thousands of brave fellows who have wrought out this glorious problem, spite of changes, storms, and even doubts of the incredulous, and all the obstacles you have now happily surmounted.

W. T. SHERMAN, *General.*

That night the visitors started east and west, leaving the engineers and working parties to arrange the details for conducting the business of each road at this terminal. It was only a day or two before trains bound for the Atlantic and Pacific were passing regularly.

During the building of the road from Sherman west, many questions arose in relation to the location, construction, the grades and curvatures of the work. All through I stood firmly for my line, for what I considered was a commercially economical line for the company, and for what I thought we ought to build under the specifications of the Government. News of the contest between the company and the contractors reached Washington through the government commissioners. Generals Grant and Sherman were much interested, and in 1868 they came West with a party consisting of Maj. Gen. Philip H. Sheridan, Gen. August Kautz, Gen. Joseph C. Potter, Gen. Frederick Dent, Gen. William S. Harney, Gen. Louis C. Hunt, Gen. Adam Slemmer, Sidney Dillon, and T. C. Durant, who wired me to meet them at Fort Sanders, then the headquarters of General Gibbon. The questions in dispute between myself and the contractors were then taken up, and Generals Grant and Sherman took decided grounds in the matter, supporting me fully, so that I had no further trouble. A view of this gathering of officers was caught by a local photographer who happened to be at the post, and is reproduced here. Probably no more noted military gathering has occurred since the civil war.

Two changes were made by the contractors in the line so as to cheapen the work, and this was at the expense of the commercial value of the property. This was always opposed by the division engineer who located the line, and he was supported by the chief engineer. The changes were always made when the chief engineer was absent. The company would agree to a change, and the work on the changes would be so far advanced that it was too late to rectify the matter when the chief engineer returned. The first change was of Mr. James A. Evans's location on the eastern slope of the Black Hills from Cheyenne to Sherman. Evans had a 90-foot equated grade with a 6° maximum curvature. It was a very fine location, and the amount of curvature was remarkably small for a mountain line. It rose 90 feet to the mile in a steady climb. Col. Silas Seymour, the consulting engineer, undertook to reduce this grade to 80 feet, but increased the curvature so much that an engine would haul more cars over Evans's 90-foot grade than on Seymour's 80-foot grade, but Seymour was obliged, when he reached the foot of the mountains, to put in a 90-foot grade to save work as he dropped off the foothills to the plains, and a portion of this grade remains to-day. When Evans took up the change in his report and compared it with his line, he made it so plain that the change was wrong that the government directors adopted it for their report.

The next change was from Laramie River to Rattlesnake Hills, or Carbon Summit. The original line ran north of Cooper Lake, and O'Neil, who had instructions to locate on that line, changed it, by order of Col. Silas Seymour, consulting engineer, to a line dropping into the valleys of Rock Creek and Medicine Bow River, to save work. This increased the length of the line 20 miles and caused the report that we were making the road crooked to gain mileage and secure $48,000 per mile of the bonded subsidy. The amount of grading on this line was about one-half of that on the original line. During 1903 and 1904, in bringing the Union Pacific line down to a maximum grade of 47 feet to the mile, except over the Wasatch Range and Black Hills, the company abandoned this principal change made by the consulting engineer, and built on or near my original location, saving about 20 miles in distance. It was this change that brought Generals Grant and Sherman to see me and insist on my remaining as chief engineer. At the time this change was made the chief engineer was in Salt Lake, and did not know of

TEMPORARY TRESTLE, PROMONTORY, UTAH.

it until it was practically graded. He entered his protest and notified the company that he would not submit to such changes without being consulted.

I remember that the progress of the work was then such that Generals Grant and Sherman were very enthusiastic over the belief that we would soon reach the summit of the Wasatch Mountains, but I could not convince them that a junction of the two roads was in sight within a year. When you consider that not a mile of this division of the road had been located on April 1, 1868; that not a mile of this work had been opened; that we covered in that year over 700 miles of road and built 555 and laid 589 miles of track, bringing all of our material from the Missouri River, it is no wonder that Generals Grant and Sherman could not understand how the problem before us would be so speedily solved. As each 100 miles of road was completed there came a general acclaim from all parts of the country to our great encouragement, while from our chiefs in New York there was a continual pressure for speed, they giving us unlimited means and allowing us to stretch our forces out hundreds of miles, no matter what additional cost it made to each mile of road. Then we had the sympathy of the whole Mormon Church with us, President Young giving the matter personal attention, and seeing that the line over the Wasatch Mountains down the canyon and westward was covered by Mormons, to whom we let contracts, and we had the additional incentive that the Central Pacific was coming east nearly as fast as we were going west.

We had only one controversy with the Mormons, who had been our friends and had given the full support of the church from the time of our first reconnoissances until the final completion. It was our desire and the demand of the Mormons that we should build through Salt Lake City, and we bent all our energies to find a feasible line passing through that city and around the south end of Great Salt Lake and across the desert to Humboldt Wells, a controlling point in the line. We found the line so superior on the north of the lake that we had to adopt that route with a view of building a branch to Salt Lake City, but Brigham Young would not have this, and appealed over my head to the board of directors, who referred the question to the government directors, who fully sustained me. Then Brigham Young gave his allegiance and aid to the Central Pacific, hoping to bring them around the south end of the lake and force us to connect with them there. He even went so far as to deliver in the tabernacle a great sermon denouncing me, and stating a road could not be built or run without the aid of the Mormons. When the Central Pacific engineers made their survey they, too, were forced to adopt a line north of the lake. Then President Young returned to his first love, the Union Pacific, and turned all his forces and aid to that road.

During the building of the road the question of bridging the Missouri River was under discussion, and continuous examinations of the river in sounding, watching currents, etc., was had. Three points were finally determined upon as most feasible. First, Childs Mill, which was a high bridge, the shortest, and reached Muddy Creek with a 35-foot grade, avoiding the heavy 66-foot grade at Omaha; second, Telegraph Pole, right where there was some rock bottom, this to be a low drawbridge; and third, The M. & M. crossing for a high bridge. The latter was decided upon more especially to meet the views of Omaha, and for aid that city gave the company. We began work on the bridge in 1868, and continued it in 1869 and 1870, but the company found it impossible to continue, as they had no funds, and they could not issue any securities under their charter to pay for the work. I was very anxious the bridge should be built to utilize the thousand acres of land I had bought for our terminals in Iowa, and to fix permanently and practically the terminus in Iowa. The company proposed to me to organize a bridge company to interest the Iowa roads terminating at Council Bluffs, and ask authority from the Government to construct the bridge and issue securities upon it, the Union Pacific agreeing to use the bridge and make its terminals and connections with the Iowa roads on the Iowa side. I incorporated the Council Bluffs Railway and Missouri Bridge Company, and went before Congress for permission to bridge the Missouri River at the M. & M. crossing. I saw all the Iowa roads. They agreed to give their aid, but made the condition that their connection with the Union Pacific should be on the Iowa side. I went to Washington, presented the bill, passed it through the House, and left it in Senator Harlan's hands to pass it in the Senate. This was very quietly done, but Omaha got alarmed, and Governor Saunders, who was a personal friend of Senator Harlan, took the matter up, and, I think, went to Washington. The Omaha people interested themselves in stirring up opposition in Council Bluffs. A public meeting was held at the corner of Broadway and Pearl streets, over which Mr. J. W. Crawford presided. I was very seriously criticised and the independent bridge scheme denounced, the contention being that the bridge should be a part of the Union Pacific, although it was entirely and solely in the interests of Council Bluffs, and would have brought the terminus and business of the Union Pacific to the Bluffs, as they had entered into an agreement with the Iowa roads to that effect. The public meeting was addressed in favor of the bridge by Messrs. Pusey, Officer, and myself, also Mr. Caleb Baldwin and others, and was opposed by Messrs. James Montgomery, Larimer, and others.

The meeting passed resolutions asking our Senators to defeat the bridge bill. Senator Harlan acted on this resolution and defeated the bill in the Senate, and Saunders and Omaha accomplished their work. The Union Pacific Company was greatly disgusted and disappointed, and dropped for the time all efforts to build a bridge. If the bill had passed the bridge would have been built in the interests of Council Bluffs and the Iowa roads. The Union Pacific later on applied to Congress, which passed a bill authorizing the Union Pacific to build a bridge, issue bonds and stock upon it, the interest upon them to be paid from the revenue of the bridge, and placed it entirely in their control, but the Union Pacific had no great interest in coming to Council Bluffs or Iowa, and made their terminus at Omaha, and forced the Iowa roads over the bridge until 1875, when the United States Supreme Court decided that the Union Pacific should be operated from Council Bluffs westward as a continuous line for all purposes of communication, travel, and transportation, and especially ordered them to start all through passenger and freight trains westward-bound from the Bluffs. This came too late to cure the mischief the town meeting had accomplished, as the Union Pacific had its interests centered in Omaha, its offices located there, and the Iowa roads had made their contracts and gone there, and the Bluffs has only reaped the benefit of its terminal that the growth of business has forced to them, whereas by law, by economy of operation, and by the ample terminals made to accommodate it, it should have been the actual terminus, and should have received full benefit of it, not only from traffic of the Union Pacific, but from the traffic and interest of the Iowa roads. The Union Pacific completed the first bridge crossing the Missouri River and opened it for traffic on March 22, 1872.

One of the most difficult problems we had to solve was to keep sufficient material at the terminals to supply the daily demand. This work fell to Webster Snyder and his assistant, H. M. Hoxie, who had charge of the operation of the completed road. They were both young men in the business then, but have been at the head of great corporations since. They performed their work successfully and with ability. Hoxie said to me once, in answer to a question:

We do not take our hand off the throttle night or day until we know the front is supplied.

The operating department also had the Indians to contend with. An illustration of this came to me after our track had passed Plum Creek, 200 miles west of the Missouri River. The Indians had captured a freight train and were in possession of it and its crews. It so happened that I was coming down from the front with my car, which was a traveling arsenal. At Plum Creek station word came of this capture and stopped us. On my train were perhaps 20 men, some a portion of the crew, some who had been discharged and sought passage to the rear. Nearly all were strangers to me. The excitement of the capture and the reports coming by telegraph of the burning of the train brought all men to the platform, and when I called upon them to fall in, to go forward and retake the train, every man on the train went into line, and by his position showed that he was a soldier. We ran down slowly until we came in sight of the train. I gave the order to deploy as skirmishers, and at the command they went forward as steadily and in as good order as we had seen the old soldiers climb the face of Kenesaw under fire.

Nearly all the engineers and chiefs of the different units of the construction of the line have risen to distinction in their profession since the road was built. The chiefs of the parties were S. B. Reed, F. M. Case, James A. Evans, Percy T. Brown, L. L. Hills (the two latter killed by the Indians), J. E. House, M. F. Hurd, Thomas H. Bates, F. C. Hodges, James R. Maxwell, John O'Neil, Francis E. Appleton, Col. J. O. Hudnut, J. F. McCabe, Mr. Morris, and Jacob Blickensderfer.

Our principal geologist was David Van Lennep, whose reports upon the geology of the country from the Missouri River to the Pacific have been remarkably verified in later and more detailed examinations.

The superintendents of construction were S. B. Reed and James A. Evans, both of whom had been connected with the road since 1864. They had independent and thorough organizations. Mr. S. B. Reed was a very competent engineer and had had large experience in his profession. He was very successful in utilizing the Mormons in his work west of the Green River. Mr. Reed and Mr. Hurd afterwards made some of the most difficult locations over the mountain ranges for the Canadian Pacific.

Mr. Reed's principal assistant was M. F. Hurd, who served in the Second Iowa Infantry during the civil war. I detailed him on my staff as an engineer, and, although a private, he won distinction in all the campaigns for his ability, nerve, bravery, and modesty. On the Union Pacific, as well as other transcontinental lines with which he has been connected, he has performed some remarkable engineering work. He has had to fight many times for the lives of himself and party, and, no matter what odds have been against him, he has never failed to maintain his position and win his battles, though at times the chances looked desperate.

S. B. REED.
Superintendent of Construction, Union Pacific Railway.

GENERAL J. S. CASEMENT.

Casement Brothers laid all the track and did a large part of the grading of the Union Pacific Railway.

How We Built The Union Pacific.

The track laying on the Union Pacific was a science. Mr. W. A. Bell, in an article on the Pacific Railroads, describes, after witnessing it, as follows:

We, pundits of the far East, stood upon that embankment, only about a thousand miles this side of sunset, and backed westward before that hurrying corps of sturdy operators with a mingled feeling of amusement, curiosity, and profound respect. On they came. A light car, drawn by a single horse, gallops up to the front with its load of rails. Two men seize the end of a rail and start forward, the rest of the gang taking hold by twos, until it is clear of the car. They come forward at a run. At the word of command the rail is dropped in its place, right side up with care, while the same process goes on at the other side of the car. Less than thirty seconds to a rail for each gang, and so four rails go down to the minute. Quick work, you say, but the fellows on the Union Pacific are tremendously in earnest. The moment the car is empty it is tipped over on the side of the track to let the next loaded car pass it, and then it is tipped back again; and it is a sight to see it go flying back for another load, propelled by a horse at full gallop at the end of 60 or 80 feet of rope, ridden by a young Jehu, who drives furiously. Close behind the first gang come the gaugers, spikers, and bolters, and a lively time they make of it. It is a grand "anvil chorus" that those sturdy sledges are playing across the plains. It is in a triple time, three strokes to the spike. There are 10 spikes to a rail, 400 rails to a mile, 1,800 miles to San Francisco—21,000,000 times are those sledges to be swung; 21,000,000 times are they to come down with their sharp punctuation before the great work of modern America is complete.

The entire track and a large part of the grading on the Union Pacific Railway was done by the Casement Brothers—Gen. Jack Casement and Dan Casement. General Casement had been a prominent brigade and division commander in the western army. Their force consisted of 100 teams and 1,000 men, living at the end of the track in boarding cars and tents, and moved forward with it every few days. It was the best organized, best equipped, and best disciplined track force I have ever seen. I think every chief of the different units of the force had been an officer of the army, and entered on this work the moment they were mustered out. They could lay from 1 to 3 miles of track per day, as they had material, and one day laid $8\frac{1}{2}$ miles. Their rapidity in track laying, as far as I know, has never been excelled. I used it several times as a fighting force, and it took no longer to put it into fighting-line than it did to form it for its daily work. They not only had to lay and surface the track, but had to bring forward to the front from each base all the material and supplies for the track and for all workmen in advance of the track. Bases were organized for the delivery of material generally from 100 to 200 miles apart, according to the facilities for operation. These bases were as follows: First, Fremont; second, Fort Kearney; third, North Platte; fourth, Julesburg; fifth, Sidney; sixth, Cheyenne; seventh, Laramie; eighth, Benton (the last crossing of the

North Platte); ninth, Green River; tenth, Evanston; eleventh, Ogden; and, finally, Promontory.

At these bases large towns were established, which moved forward with the bases, and many miles of sidings were put in for switching purposes, unloading tracks, etc. At these prominent points I have seen as many as a thousand teams waiting for their loads to haul forward to the front for the railway force, the Government, and for the limited population then living in that country. I have seen these terminal towns starting first with a few hundred people until at Cheyenne, at the base of the mountains, where we wintered in 1867–68, there were 10,000 people. From that point they decreased until at Green River there were not over 1,000. After we crossed the first range of mountains we moved our bases so rapidly they could not afford to move with us.

In 1865 Oakes and Oliver Ames, of Boston, became interested in the enterprise, bringing their own fortune and a very large following, and really gave the first impetus to the building of the road. There was no man connected with it who devoted his time and money with the single purpose of benefit to the country and Government more than Oakes Ames, and there was never a more unjust, uncalled for, and ungrateful act of Congress than that which censured him for inducing, as it is claimed, Members of Congress to take interest in the construction company. When they took it there was no necessity for the company having influence in Congress, for there was nothing we could ask that Congress did not give, and it certainly never occurred to him that he might secure benefits from their votes. Now that the Government has been paid every dollar that it invested, with interest, it is time that the Congress of the United States should wipe that unjust act from its record.

The instructions given me by Oliver Ames, the president of the company, were invariably to obtain the best line the country afforded, regardless of the expense. Oakes Ames once wrote me, when it seemed almost impossible to raise money to meet our expenditures:

Go ahead; the work shall not stop, even if it takes the shovel shop.

The Ameses were manufacturers of shovels and tools, and their fortunes were invested in that business; and, as we all know, the shovel shop went. When the day came that the business of the Ameses should go or the Union Pacific, Oakes Ames said:

Save the credit of the road; I will fail.

It took a man of courage and patriotism to make that decision and lay down a reputation and business credit that was invaluable in New England, and one that had come down through almost a century. To him it was worse than death; and it was the blow given by the action of Congress which, followed by others, put him in his grave.

In February, 1875, Mr. Jay Gould, who had become heavily interested in the Union Pacific Railway, in connection with Messrs. Ames, Dillon, and the board of directors, conceived a plan of paying to the Government in addition to the sum it was then receiving from the company a sum of money each year that should be used as a sinking fund, which, at the maturity of the government bond, would liquidate that indebtedness. The Hon. James F. Wilson, of Iowa, a government director, and myself were selected to go to Washington to present the matter to the Government. General Grant was then President, and Gen. Benjamin F. Bristow Secretary of the Treasury. We presented the proposition to General Grant, who looked upon it favorably and referred it to the Secretary of the Treasury for the purpose of having a bill drawn which would carry out our views. The entire Cabinet was in favor of the proposition with the single exception of Mr. Jewell, of Connecticut. Upon the report of General Bristow, General Grant drafted a message to the Congress of the United States, recommending the passage of an act that would carry out this plan.

In the meantime rumors of what we were doing had reached New York, where there was a large short interest in the stock of the Union Pacific. This interest immediately gathered its forces and influence and sent persons to Washington to represent to the President that the proposed action of the Union Pacific was a mere stock-jobbing scheme for the purpose of twisting the shorts on Union Pacific stock, and their representations made such an impression on General Grant that he never sent his message in, and the company, receiving the treatment it did, then abandoned for the time all efforts to make a settlement with the Government. General Grant often said to me in later years that he regretted he did not settle the matter at that time. This demonstrates that at the moment the Union Pacific began to be prosperous the men who put their money in it and built it made the first effort to pay the debt due the Government at or before its maturity. If their offer had been accepted the earnings of the company demonstrated that they would have been able to have met their agreement, and at the maturity of the debt it would have been paid. This is one of the many instances in which the Union Pacific Railway has endeavored to fulfill, not only in letter, but in spirit, every obligation it owed to the Government, and I undertake to say that the Government of the United States, from the time the road was finally completed and in continuous operation, has never fulfilled any one of its obligations to the company, except the simple giving of its credit at the time of the building by the issue of its bonds.

How We Built The Union Pacific.

How well our work was performed is shown by the reports of the distinguished commissions appointed by the Government to examine the road during its construction and after its completion.

Commissioners Horace Walbridge, S. M. Felton, C. B. Comstock, E. F. Winslow, and J. F. Boyd examined the road in 1869 to ascertain the sum of money that was necessary to complete the road under the government specifications, and the sum found necessary on the Union Pacific was $1,586,100, and on the Central Pacific $576,650. The amount required on the Union Pacific was only about one-half as much as the chief engineer of that road had found necessary to complete the road under the company's own specifications, and the company not only spent this, but a much larger sum in the work.

The last commission, composed of Maj. Gen. G. K. Warren, U. S. Army; J. Blickensderfer, jr., and James Barnes, civil engineers, concluded their report in part, as follows:

The foregoing shows that the location of the Union Pacific Railway is in accordance with the law, and as a whole and in its different parts the most direct, central, and practicable that would be found from Omaha to the head of Great Salt Lake. Taken as a whole, the Union Pacific Railway has been well constructed. The energy and perseverance with which the work has been urged forward, and the rapidity with which it has been executed, was without parallel in history. In grandeur and magnitude of the undertaking it has never been equaled, and the country has reason to congratulate itself upon this great work of national importance so rapidly approaching completion under such favorable auspices.

When the Canadian government determined to build a Pacific railway, they had the Union Pacific examined, and after that examination they provided in their contracts that the Canadian Pacific should be built upon the Union Pacific standards, and when completed should be in its location and construction equal to it, thus paying a high compliment to the builders of the Union Pacific, and after the completion of the Canadian Pacific Railway, engineers of the Union Pacific were selected to examine that road to determine if its construction was up to the standard required.

The Blickensderfer and Clement report made a comparative analysis of the Union Pacific and Central Pacific, their location, construction, grade, curvature, etc., giving to the Union Pacific credit for being superior in most of these matters. The last and most critical examination of the location, grades, etc., came within the last three years, when under the reorganized company it was determined to reduce the grades to a maximum of 47 feet going east or west except at two points, the 80-foot grade at Cheyenne going west, and the 80-foot grade at the head of Echo Canyon going east.

The president of the Union Pacific, Mr. E. H. Harriman, at a banquet in Denver in 1904 stated that after the three years' examination, and the expenditure of $15,000,000 to $20,000,000 to change the grades to a maximum of 47 feet to the mile, it had been demonstrated that not a mile of road had been built to increase the distance and obtain subsidies; that the location and construction was a credit to the engineers and executive officers who built the road.

Mr. J. B. Berry, chief engineer of the Union Pacific Railroad, who had charge of the changes, pays this tribute to the engineers of the road:

It may appear to those unfamiliar with the character of the country that the great saving in distance and reduction of grade would stand as a criticism of the work of the pioneer engineers who made the original location of the road. Such is not the case. The changes made have been expensive and could be warranted only by the volume of traffic handled at the present day. Too much credit can not be given Gen. G. M. Dodge and his assistants. They studied their task thoroughly and performed it well. Limited by law to a maximum gradient of 116 feet to the mile, not compensated for curvature, they held it down to about 90 feet per mile. Taking into consideration the existing conditions thirty-five years ago, lack of maps of the country, hostility of the Indians, which made United States troops necessary for protection of surveying parties, difficult transportation, excessive cost of labor, uncertainty as to probable volume of traffic, limited amount of money and necessity to get the road built as soon as possible, it can be said, with all our present knowledge of the topography of the country, that the line was located with very great skill.

The principal changes made by the Union Pacific Railroad since 1900 was, first, the change from the Muddy Creek line out of Omaha to the original Dey line, now known as the Lane cut-off, which saves 11 miles in 14 miles distance. The next is the line from Sherman to the Laramie plains, where by long tunnels and heavy work the grade is reduced from 90 feet to 47 feet maximum. The third change is the Cooper Lake line, which is changed from Rock Creek and Medicine Bow to near the original location of the Union Pacific, with a saving of 20 miles in distance. This is the change made when the line was building by the contractors against the protest of the chief engineer of the road and caused Generals Grant and Sherman to come to Fort Sanders for a conference. The fourth change was on the Central Pacific road from Ogden across Bear Creek, arm of Salt Lake, known as Lucien cut-off, saving 50 miles in distance and avoiding the heavy grades over Promontory Point. The original survey of the Union Pacific was from Ogden across Bear Creek, arm of Salt Lake, to south end of Promontory Point, but, as stated in another part of this paper, was abandoned because of the 12 feet of higher water in the lake in 1869, when the line was built, than in 1900, when the change was made. I understand the lake has been rising about 1 foot a year since this cut-off was completed. In a letter which I received from Mr. James R. Maxwell, assistant engineer, he makes the following statement of the result of their survey in 1867:

The boat we used in sounding the lake was made of inch boards and not calked very well, and the heavy water soon shook the calking out of the bottom, and it did seem for a short time that we would have to take to the water. That was on our way back from Promontory Point to Mud Island. After we landed the topographer told me that he could not swim; if I had known that he would not have been on the boat. When I found 22 feet of water where Captain Stansbury had only 10 I knew that that line was not feasible then. I was told by a Mormon bishop that on two occasions the annual rise was 6 feet above any previous record and that it remained so, covering thousands of acres of farming land at northeastern side of the lake.

This part of the lake that was sounded by this party was east of Promontory Point. The water to the west of Promontory Point being twice as deep as that toward the east, therefore it was impossible for us with our means to build a railroad across the lake and we were forced around the north end of the lake and over Promontory Point.

The first surveys of the Union Pacific Railway were made in the fall of 1853. The first grading was done in the fall of 1864. The first rail was laid in July, 1865. Two hundred and sixty miles were built in 1866, 240 in 1867, including the ascent of the first range of mountains to an elevation of 8,235 feet above sea level, and from April 1, 1868, to May 10, 1869, 555 miles of road was built, all exclusive of temporary track and sidings, of which over 180 miles was built in addition, all at an approximate cost in cash of about $54,000,000.

Of late years there has been a great deal of criticism and comparison of the building of the Union Pacific and Central Pacific railroads, favoring the latter. The theory is that because the Central Pacific had the Sierra Nevada Range to tackle at first, it was a more difficult problem financially and physically to handle than the Union Pacific end, but this is a very great mistake. The Union Pacific had to bring all of its material, ties, bridging, etc., from tide water by rail or by river. They had to build the first 630 miles without any material on its line to aid them except the earth, and for this they only received $16,000 per mile in government bonds. There was no settlement on the line to create any traffic or earnings along the whole distance, which was very difficult in appealing to the people to buy the bonds and furnish money for the company. In comparison to this, the Central Pacific started at Sacramento with a tidewater base coming right up to it, so that all the material that had to come from foreign or domestic ports had the cheapest rates by sea. Then from Sacramento they had built over the mountains to Virginia City to the great Bonanza mines at Virginia City, which gave them a large traffic at high rates, and gave them very large earnings. Then, again, only a few miles east of Sacramento, the east base of the Sierra Nevada Range commences, and they received immediately $48,000 in government bonds per mile for the 150 miles, and $32,000 in government bonds from there on to Salt Lake, a distance of barely 200 miles, more than the 630 miles that the Union Pacific had to build on $16,000 per mile. This favorable condition for the Central Pacific was such that the representatives of that road had very little difficulty in raising all the money they needed and having for nearly one-half of their road a fine traffic to help pay the interest on their bonds.

I do not speak of this in criticism of the work of the Central Pacific, which was remarkable, and like that of the Union Pacific, has never been excelled, but only in comparison of the difficulties the two companies had to overcome. I am not surprised that some of the public should take this view of the matter when the later literature of the Union Pacific seems to take the same view and devote what praise it has to the work of the men who built the Central Pacific, overlooking almost entirely the struggles of those who initiated the work on the line of the Union Pacific and who furnished the funds to explore the country and determine the feasibility of the route and stood by it for nearly twelve years before the Central Pacific was thought of. The fact is, the Central Pacific obtained no right and did not think of going east of the California state line until after the laws of 1865 and 1866 had been enacted, which gave them the right to come east of the state line of California and made them a part of the transcontinental line.

The operation of the road the first winter, 1869–70, gave us a test of what we might expect from the snow. In building the road, we studied the mountains to get our lines upon the slopes that were the least exposed to heavy snows and slides, but we had no means of fighting the snows in the Laramie Plains except by fences and sheds, and none were put up until the year 1870, so that when the heavy snows fell in the winter of 1869–70 it caught six of our trains west of Laramie that were snowed in there some weeks. As a precaution in starting our trains from Omaha, we put on a box car with a stove in it and loaded with provisions, so as to meet any emergency. These six trains that were caught in the snow between Laramie and the divide of the continent had these supplies and also were supplied with sledges and snowshoes from Laramie. They had with them, in charge of the six trains, Mr. H. M. Hoxie, the assistant superintendent, who managed to get the trains together, but the blizzards were so many and so fierce that it was impossible for men to work out in the open, and even when they cleared the cuts ahead they would fill up before they could get the trains through them. Probably that winter's experience with snow was the worst the Union Pacific has ever experienced, but Mr. Hoxie handled his forces with great ability and fed and entertained his passengers in good shape. In one train was an opera company bound for California that Mr. Hoxie used to entertain the passengers with, so that when the trains reached Salt Lake City the passengers held a meeting and passed resolutions complimentary to Mr. Hoxie and the Union Pacific in bringing them safely through. A photograph of the trains was taken at the time they were snowed in near Cooper Lake, and a print of it is here reproduced.

I can not conclude this description of the building of the Union Pacific Railway better than quoting my conclusions, as stated in my final report, sent to the company and the United States Government on December 1, 1869. It is as follows:

" In 1853 Henry Farnam and T. C. Durant, the then contractors and builders of the Missouri River Railroad in Iowa, instructed Peter A. Dey to investigate the question of the proper point for the Mississippi and Missouri River road to strike the Missouri River to obtain a good connection with any road that might be built across the continent. I was assigned to the duty, and surveys were accordingly extended to and up the Platte Valley, to ascertain whether any road built on the central or then northern line would, from the formation of the country, follow the Platte and its tributaries over the plains, and thus overcome the Rocky Mountains. Subsequently, under the patronage of Mr. Farnam, I extended the examination westward to the eastern base of the Rocky Mountains and beyond, examining the practicable passes from the Sangre Christo to the South Pass; made maps of the country, and developed it as thoroughly as could be done without making purely instrumental surveys. The practicability of the route, the singular formation of the country between Long's Peak, the Medicine Bow Mountains, and Bridger Pass, on the south, and Laramie Peak and the Sweetwater and Wind River ranges on the north, demonstrated to me that through this region the road must eventually be built. I reported the facts to Mr. Farnam, and through his and his friends' efforts, the prospect for a Pacific railroad began to take shape.

" In after years, when the war demonstrated the road to be a military necessity, and the Government gave its aid in such munificent grants, surveys were extended through the country previously explored, its resources developed, its hidden treasures brought to light, and its capabilities for the building of a railway to the Pacific fully demonstrated.

SIX PASSENGER TRAINS SNOWED IN ON THE LARAMIE PLAINS.

Union Pacific Railway, winter of 1869-70.

" In doing this over the country extending from the Missouri River to the California state line, and covering a width of 200 miles, north and south, and on the general direction of the forty-second parallel of latitude, some 15,000 miles of instrumental lines have been run, and over 25,000 miles of reconnoissances made.

" In 1863 and 1864, surveys were inaugurated, but in 1866 the country was systematically occupied; and day and night, summer and winter, the explorations were pushed forward through dangers and hardships that very few at this day appreciate, for every mile had to be run within range of the musket, as there was not a moment's security. In making the surveys numbers of our men, some of them the ablest and most promising, were killed; and during the construction our stock was run off by the hundred, I might say, by the thousand, and as one difficulty after another arose and was overcome, both in the engineering and running and constructing departments, a new era in railroad building was inaugurated.

" Each day taught us lessons by which we profited for the next, and our advances and improvements in the art of railway construction were marked by the progress of the work, 40 miles of track having been laid in 1865, 260 in 1866, 240 in 1867, including the ascent to the summit of the Rocky Mountains, at an elevation of 8,235 feet above the ocean; and during 1868, and to May 10, 1869, 555 miles, all exclusive of side and temporary tracks, of which over 180 miles were built in addition.

" The first grading was done in the autumn of 1864, and the first rail laid in July, 1865. When you look back to the beginning at the Missouri River, with no railway communication from the East, and 500 miles of the country in advance without timber, fuel, or any material whatever from which to build or maintain a road, except the sand for the bare roadbed itself, with everything to be transported, and that by teams or at best by steamboats, for hundreds and thousands of miles; everything to be created, with labor scarce and high, you can all look back upon the work with satisfaction and ask, Under such circumstances could we have done more or better!

" The country is evidently satisfied that you accomplished wonders, and have achieved a work that will be a monument to your energy, your ability, and to your devotion to the enterprise through all its gloomy as well as its bright periods, for it is notorious that notwithstanding the aid of the Government there was so little faith in the enterprise that its dark days—when your private fortunes and your all was staked on the success of the project—far exceeded those of sunshine, faith, and confidence.

" This lack of confidence in the project, even in the West, in those localities where the benefits of its construction were manifest, was excessive, and it will be remembered that laborers even demanded their pay before they would perform their day's work, so little faith had they in the payment of their wages, or in the ability of the company to succeed in their efforts. Probably no enterprise in the world has been so maligned, misrepresented, and criticised as this; but now, after the calm judgment of the American people is brought to bear upon it, unprejudiced and unbiased, it is almost without exception pronounced the best new road in the United States.

" Its location has been critically examined, and although the route was in a comparatively short time determined upon, as compared with that devoted to other similar projects, yet, in regard to the correctness of the general route, no question is ever raised; and even in the details of its location, 730 miles of which were done in less than six months, it has received the praise of some of the ablest engineers of the country. Its defects are minor ones, easily remedied, and all the various commissions, some of them composed of able and noted engineers, have given the company due credit in this particular, although they may have attacked it in others, and to-day, as in the past, the company need fear no fair, impartial criticism upon it or no examination made by men of ability and integrity or such as are masters of their profession.

" That it yet needs work to finally complete it no one denies, but whatever is necessary has been or is being done.

" Its future is fraught with great good. It will develop a waste, will bind together the two extremes of the nation as one, will stimulate intercourse and trade and bring harmony, prosperity, and wealth to the two coasts. A proper policy, systematically and persistently followed, will bring to the road the trade of the two oceans, and will give it all the business it can accommodate, while the local trade will increase gradually until the mining, grazing, and agricultural regions through which it passes will build up and create a business that will be a lasting and permanent support to the country."

CITY OF ROCKS.

Northwest of Salt Lake, on Union Pacific Railway survey to Oregon, 1868.